GW00382022

The Devil and the Floral Dance

fal

fal

Award-winning books from Cornwall

Dear Shadows	DM Thomas
Keeping House	Bill Mycock
Olga's Dreams	Victoria Field
Sleeping in the Rain	St Petrocs
Once in a Blue Moon	Angela Stoner

www.falpublications.co.uk

The Devil and the Floral Dance

D. M. Thomas

fal

Second, revised edition 2006

| Copyright | text | DM Thomas |
| | illustrations | Linda Selby |

All rights reserved

ISBN 0-9544980-5-4

Published by
fal publications
PO Box 74
Truro
TR1 1XS

www.falpublications.co.uk

Printed by

R. Booth
Antron Hill
Mabe
Cornwall

The Devil and the Floral Dance was first published by Robson
Books Ltd., London, 1978, with illustrations by John Alstrop.
The text has been revised for this new edition.

D.M.Thomas
Truro, February 2006

For my grandchildren,
Sorcha, Angus and Lucy

The Devil and the Floral Dance

D. M. Thomas

fal

1

Strange things happen where the sea and the land meet. Maybe this is because nothing is ever still. The waves are breaking against the cliffs, the clouds move a little faster than they do inland, driven by the sea-wind. The light of the sun or the moon changes from minute to minute. And think of the strange objects cast up onto the beach, after a storm – pieces of driftwood, even gold or silver coins now and again, from ships sunk hundreds of years ago. And always, brighter than old gold coins, beautiful shells glistening on wet sand. But the strangest things of all can happen in Cornwall, where the sea is all around you ...

So, with the sea on three sides of him, just a few miles away across the bleak flat heath called Goonhilly Downs, the television engineer sitting indoors alone under the saucer-shaped radio receiver, one starry May night, ought to have been on the look-out for something strange. It was his job to keep track of all the television satellites that spin endlessly round the earth, taking Eastenders or Man U vs Chelsea to every corner of the planet. But he was a down-to-earth sort of chap, and busy oiling his cricket-bat for next Saturday's match. So the very unusual noise that crackled through the receiver took him completely by surprise. He dropped his bat and spilled the linseed-oil. He had never heard anything like it before. He wondered if the Russians or Americans, or China perhaps, had sent up a new space-craft. But if so, it must be something really new, to make this peculiar noise. It came from the south, from over the Lizard lighthouse.

He rushed out and looked up at the sky. Nothing moved there, not even a helicopter's light coming in to land on the air-field to the north, after some daring air-sea rescue. The Lizard Light flashed every few seconds, monotonously. To the west and east, over the silent, ghostly heath, he could see the slight shimmer reflected off the ocean; and northwards, past the air-field, the glow of street lights from the nearest town, Helston. All seemed well. He went back inside, and the strange signal was still there, passing overhead. Thoughtfully he began oiling his cricket bat again.

At the same moment, in the radar-room of the air-sea rescue station, HMS *Seahawk*, a young sailor was startled by a weird flying object coming from the south - and then another, farther away, coming to meet it from the north. On the radar-screen they looked alike. They seemed to have wings, like giant eagles. When they had almost met, they drifted down on the screen and vanished. He guessed they had landed in Helston. He thought of calling the duty officer, but there wasn't anything to show him anymore, and he didn't want to make a fuss over nothing. He made a note in the log-book: 'Two giant eagles flying in from opposite directions to land in or near Helston.' Then he went back to reading his thriller, and hoped for the best.

They weren't eagles, of course. They were St Michael and the Devil.
They met early the next afternoon in Helston's main street. Both blinked in surprise. They had not met for thousands of years.

'What are you doing here?' said St Michael.

'I'm on my holidays,' said the Devil.

'Summer holidays?'

'No. Winter break.'

The Devil was muffled up in a heavy black duffel coat and Wellington boots, while St Michael wore sandals, blue jeans, and a white tee-shirt. It was a typical spring day: one moment the sun drenched the grey, granite houses in bright light, the next, clouds plunged them in gloom. There were crowds of people out shopping, buying groceries for the next day, May 8th, Flora Day. Shopkeepers were busy hanging out flags and bunting. St Michael was holding the step-ladder for the white-coated chemist to fasten a Union Jack and the Cornish flag over his window filled with cough mixtures and hot water bottles. The chemist thanked him politely.

'What were you buying?' said St Michael to the Devil, nodding at the chemist's shop. 'Beechams Powders,' said the Devil.

'Stomach trouble?'

'Jet lag,' said the Devil, and his face did look a little green. He shivered inside his

duffel coat. 'Bitter weather,' he complained. 'I'm not used to the cold.'
'Goin' have drop rain, are us?' asked the chemist cheerfully, stepping down to the pavement and glancing up. St Michael knew that when a Cornishman asks you if there is going to be a drop of rain, it's ready to pelt down. Sure enough, huge drops started to fall, and got thicker by the moment. Shoppers vanished into the doorways. It was more like sleet than rain. 'Come and have a cup of tea,' St Michael invited, and took the Devil's arm to lead him at a trot to the nearest cafe.

Now, you may be rather surprised by all this, for two reasons. Angels don't have bodies - at least not like ours - and the Devil, after all, is a fallen angel. And why should St Michael and the Devil, who are deadly enemies, be chatting to each other in such a friendly way?

Well, the answers to both questions are quite simple. If you go on a foreign holiday, you like to live like the natives for a while, it's a part of the fun. You don't walk around in a raincoat eating fish and chips from a newspaper - or at least you shouldn't! Both the Archangel and the Devil were on a sort of foreign holiday, and so they enjoyed putting on flesh and blood for a day or two. The Demon was quite enjoying himself really, in spite of feeling a bit sick and dizzy after his long flight; and cold, even in his thermal underwear, after the fires of Hell.

And they were friendly because - well, they had *once* been close friends, before the Devil fell from Heaven in disgrace. In the shock of meeting again, after such a long time, the old feelings of friendliness had come to the fore.

The Devil asked the waitress to switch on the heating. She said she wasn't allowed to, as it was summer season now. The Devil grumbled, huddled over his hot tea and munched a saffron bun. 'Good!' said St Michael, smacking his lips over his bun. 'Not bad for a shop-bun,' grumbled the Devil. 'I had a pasty for lunch and it was awful - awful. All pastry and mince.' (A real Cornish pasty has big juicy chunks of beef and plenty of gravy.) 'They don't make 'em like they used to.'

St. Michael asked him if he had found anywhere to stay. 'No,' said the Devil testily, 'there isn't a room anywhere. How about you?'

'Not a hope. `Tis all they emmets, you!' (Emmets, in Cornwall, means ants, or in other words, swarms of tourists. As the patron saint of Helston and of Cornwall, St Michael liked to slip in a Cornish expression now and again.) 'I was looking forward to staying at the Angel Hotel, but nothing doing.'

The Devil cheered up. 'The Angel's full of television people,' he grinned. 'Cameramen and producers, down for the Flora like everybody else. That's what I like to see - sticking their noses in and wrecking these quaint old customs!'

St Michael rubbed his chin thoughtfully. Now he remembered why they'd fallen out, why the Devil had fallen. He called the waitress and she came with a smile and the bill. 'Some *weather*, isn't it?' she said, as the rain and sleet hammered against the glass. 'Like fate,' nodded St Michael, paying up. The Devil smiled to himself as he looked out at the rain. Secretly he was pleased. The Angel put a generous tip under his saucer. 'I'm off to the school,' he said, 'to see how the kids are getting on. Can't tempt you, I suppose?'

'Not on your life!' sneered the Devil. He remembered now why he'd quarrelled with St Michael. All his slimy nonsense about liking kids and animals and flowers and stuff. 'I'm off to visit old haunts.' (There are lots of these round the Lizard coast, dangerous places for boats and bathers, like Devil's Mouth, Devil's Letter Box, and Devil's Frying Pan.) 'See you later maybe.' He vanished. The waitress blinked, seeing only one man, the cool, goodlooking guy, leave by the door.

St Michael had a brisk walk uphill in the easing rain, and came to a building that he recognised from his last visit, in 1940, Hitler's year. Outside the gates he slipped out of his body into his invisible purple cloak, gold folded wings, and with a bright sword at his side. He walked into the school, along a corridor, and into a classroom where it sounded very noisy. He stood by the rock-table. The teacher was trying to go over the history and meaning of the Flora. It was nearly home-time. The children were feeling excited because of tomorrow's holiday.

2

'When Winter and Summer come to blows
And maids look out their flimsy clothes,'
Said the teacher, Jack Penrose,
    'We feel like a dance and a song.
Winter is strong, but Summer is lighter,
Like Bob Fitzsimmons*, the Helston fighter.
Each afternoon the sun shines brighter
    As you walk home-along.

'Shadow and light, like a giraffe, run
Over the gorse as yellow as saffron
From the Helford to Halzaphron.'
    ' Sir,' said Tommy Bone,
'There aren't no giraffes upon Goonhilly.'
'Shut your mouth, Tom, and don't be silly,
You're getting as daft as your brother Billy,
    --And leave your boil alone.

'Couples have danced up Coinagehall
Ever since folk was here at all.
So you tell your father, Mary Paull,
    Your aunt can mind the shop:
However busy it is tomorra
You'll be dancin' in the children's Flora
Up front with David and Peter and Nora
    And you'll dance till you bloomin' well drop.

*Bob Fitzsimmons: World Heavyweight Champion, 1897

'Now, how did the Flora get its name?'
'From margarine,' said Jenny Rame.
Jack threw a book but missed his aim.
      'I'll give you margarine!
Hundreds of years or more ago
They changed its name to the Flora, though
Our ancestors called it - as you know -?'
      'The Furry,' said Timothy Green.

'And Furry, sir, is an old word for
A fair or feast-day. ' 'Good! And *your*
Saint of the feast is ... ?   *Kim Treloar!*
      Wake up! ... St Michael. Right.
St Michael the Archangel's spear
Saved Helston from Old Nick. That clear?
And where did St Michael first appear?'
      'On my vest,' said Jimmy Blight.

'You great buffoon!' Jack cuffed his ear.
'Sir,' said Cora Tremaine, 'he's here,
He've got a sword, but there ain't no spear.
      He's over by they rocks.'
'Cora, I thought you were twice as deep
As Falmouth harbour, and counting sheep,
But by God you were only half asleep.
      Lord save me from these shocks!

'The bell's not gone! Stop all this din!
The Hal-an-Tow singers will begin
Tomorrow by bringing the Summer in:
      Who led them on her ass
Well, *donkey*, then? ' snapped Jack Penrose as
They oohed, 'That's *rude!*' 'Decked up in roses
Long years ago?...   Aunt Mary Moses.'
      'MOSES!' roared the rushing class.

The school was empty, everything still.
The Angel left, invisible.
The sun went down Tregonning Hill.
      Half-awake all night
Cora Tremaine half-understood
The excitement dancing in her blood.
Young people faded into the wood
      As soon as it was light.

3

It was a fine blue morning but showers were forecast. The Hal-an-Tow singers (some of them elder brothers and sisters of the children in Jack Penrose's class) turned into Cross Street in a blaze of colour, made up of the historical costumes that suited their Morning Song, and the flowers and sycamore branches they had picked in the woods.

They stopped near the ancient Celtic cross and burst into their rollicking song. Many of the spectators lining the roadside joined in. All the Cornish have good voices, and they made a merry din, enough to wake the dead in St Michael's churchyard. The words they sang were these:

Robin Hood and Little John, they both are gone to fair, O!
And we will go to the merry green wood, to see what they do there, O!
And for to chase,O! to chase the buck and doe -

Chorus:
Hal-an-Tow, Jolly Rumble, O, for we are up as soon as any day,O!
And for to fetch the summer home, the summer and the may, O!
For summer is a-come, O! and winter is a-gone, O!

Where are those Spaniards, that make so great a boast, O?
For they shall eat the grey goose feather, and we shall eat the roast, O!
In every land, O! the land where e'er we go!

Chorus: *Hal-an-Tow, Jolly Rumble, O!*

God bless Aunt Mary Moses, and all her power and might, O!
And send us peace in Merry England, both day and night, O!
And send us peace in Merry England, both now and evermore, O!

Chorus:
Hal-an-Tow, Jolly Rumble,O! for we are up as soon as any day, O!
And for to fetch the summer home, the summer and the may, O!
For summer is a-come,O! and winter is a-gone, O!

When the youngsters finished singing they walked off, bearing their song and their greenery to another part of the town. A stout middle-aged American lady said, 'Is that it?' in aggrieved tones to her equally stout husband. 'I guess so, Maude,' he growled. 'Maybe the Children's Dance will be more entertaining, honey, ' she sighed, staring short-sightedly at her programme. '1 didn't understand a word of that song,' she lamented. 'All those jolly rumble O's ... And who the heck's Aunt Mary Moses for Chri'sake?' She turned to the nice-looking young man in white tee-shirt and blue jeans who was standing next to her, chin in hand, hiding his smile: 'Can you help us, young man?'

Very politely and patiently he explained to them that this morning's procession was not meant to be an entertainment, though it was a pity they had forgotten the old 'heel-and-toe' dance that gave it its name. It was meant truly to fetch the Summer home, to bring back life into the town after the dead winter days. Like the Furry

Dances, it was older than the hills, thousands of years old. 'My O my! thousands of years!' exclaimed the American lady in awe. 'Did you hear that, Horace?' She dug Horace in the portly stomach and he doubled up slightly. 'Uh-huh,' he mumbled. Yes, said the white-shirted young man, one version said that the day's festivities were to celebrate a victory of St Michael over the Devil, and another said they were to celebrate Helston's deliverance from the plague . . . But first and foremost it was to bring in the Summer.

'That's truly wunnerful,' sighed the fat American lady. 'Isn't it, Horace?' She nudged him and he doubled up again. 'Thank you for giving us the low-down on this. You've really brought it alive. But I still don't understand the song.'

The young man explained that the words of the song were quite modern - only about three or four hundred years old! It mentioned folk-heroes like Robin Hood and St George, who (like St Michael) had overcome a dragon. It referred to the Spanish Armada: the grey goose feathers were the arrows of the English longbowmen who had conquered the might of Spain. 'That's most interesting,' she said. 'Of course we've heard of Robin Hood and St George, but Aunt Mary Moses sure has got me beat.'

Smiling, he said that 'aunt' was just an affectionate term among the Cornish; it needn't mean the lady was really your aunt. Probably she had been a well-known local character, and maybe they used her name in Puritan times when they weren't allowed to say 'God bless the holy Virgin!' In the old times, a girl or woman led the singers into town on her ass – 'donkey', he corrected hastily. 'My O my!' said the lady gushingly. 'That's really fascinating, isn't it, Horace?'

'Young man,' said Horace gravely, 'here's my card. You must look us up if you're ever in the States.' The card read 'Horace T. Winterthrush. Funeral Director and

Embalmer.' 'If you ever need my services,' grinned the portly undertaker, 'we'll give you a cut-rate!' 'Thanks a lot,' said the young man, 'but I don't think I will!' He rubbed his chin and smiled to himself as he listened out for the Helston Brass Band. As a matter of fact he was remembering lovely black-haired Mary Moses, May Queen in 1570. It wasn't a memory he could share with anyone. He also knew who the present May Queen was – or ought to be. The trouble was, nobody knew but him – and probably the Devil. She hadn't led the Hal-an-Tow ... he'd see her in a minute in the Children's Dance. There was always a May Queen, carrying the new life, as a gift from God – whether she knew it or not.

The waiting crowd had thickened, and so had the sky. There were a few drops of rain. Umbrellas went up. Faintly they heard the tumpity-tump of the band on its way, leading the Children's Dance through Church Street. Even Horace T. Winterthrush's heart quickened, hearing the famous old tune. He took a watch from his waistcoat. 'Half past ten,' he announced. 'A good time for the first dance of the day. Gives folk plenty of time for a leisurely breakfast, if they feel like skipping the Hal-an-Tow, and time for a coffee back at the hotel before the midday dance. I hope the rain holds off. If it gets worse, honey, I vote we take a nap and maybe watch the rest of the programme on TV this evening.'

'This isn't the first dance,' said the young man. 'That was at seven. I dare say you were fast asleep. You can watch that on TV too.'

The tune got louder, turned the corner into their street. The crowd pushed forward, craning their necks. Mrs Winterthrush was sent shooting forward, her specs flying from

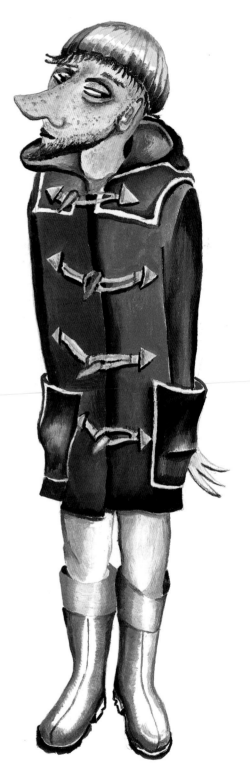

her face: the polite young man swooped like a hawk and caught them just before they hit the ground. Mrs Winterthrush sprawled on her hands and knees, huge bottom in the air. The man in a black duffel coat and Wellington boots helped Mr Winterthrush to lift her to her feet and dust her down. He was most apologetic for having pushed her. It was the crowd surging forward. 'How dreadful!' he said. 'You've ruined your fur coat, torn your stockings and cut your hand! I'm most frightfully sorry!'

'That's okay,' she gasped. "I don't care so long as my glasses aren't busted. I'd be lost without them.' She thanked the white-shirted young man profusely for saving them. 'My!' she exclaimed. 'Don't you move fast?' He shrugged and said he just happened to be very acrobatic because he'd been training with the paras. 'Look,' he said, 'here comes the band, blowing and thumping away for all they're worth! And there's the children – don't they look handsome?'

Mr Winterthrush wasn't looking. He was feeling through his pockets, worried, wondering if he could have left his wallet at the hotel ...

4

Peter Trebilcock
proud as a peacock
Mary Paull
not nervous at all,
David Angwin
gives Nora a grin
Nora Tyack
grins at him back,
Church St. to Cross St.
on this May morn,
the first four dancers
Helston-born,
dressed in white
from head to toe,
in and out of the
houses they go,
craning their necks
for uncles and aunts,
altogether in
the Children's Dance!
Jennifer Rame
is light as a flame
Jimmy Blight
hasn't slept all night,
Cora Tremaine
is fresh as rain
Tony from Rangoon
is tanned as June,
checking, and turning
their partners round
four by four
as the drum-beats pound,
the trumpets blare
and trombones boom,
into the hall
and the drawing-room,
love a lemonade
but not a chance,
altogether in
the Children's Dance!
Stephen Shore
wanted Kim Treloar

but Mary Malgrue
will have to do,
Tommy Bone
stout as a stone
Morwenna Daddow
thin as a shadow,
straightens her garland
upon her hair,
rain on the Flora –
no aches for a year,
kitchen to garden
big bass drum
getting loud enough
to make Kingdom come,
skip through puddles
mud on their pants,
altogether in
the Children's Dance!
in at the front gate
out at the back
so many turnings
they're losing track,
light over Mount's Bay,
or is it Redruth?
Andrew by Sharon
and Tim by Ruth,
hoping it's fine
for the afternoon fair,
see you by the Waltzers,
I'll be there,
through musty parlours
the children wind,
old grannies smiling,
deaf and blind,
Linda Tregonning
sees Robert Nance
only with her fingers
never a glance,
shy as the may,
sweet as a cherry,
altogether in
the Helston Furry!
Into Paull's the Florists
open for the tourists,

SEND SOME FLOWERS TO SURREY
BY INTERFLORA FERRY!
Lilies of the valley
over the heart,
break into the rich house,
take the joint apart!
soaking wet feet
bring in the summer,
call out the lifeboat,
ring up the plumber!
Pretty Chinese lady
in a frame,
must be worth a fortune,
says Jenny Rame,
dashes to the bushes
Bert the cornet-player,
never stops blowing,
catches up the rear,
music's good for growing
handsomer plants
stretching their leaves
in the Floral Dance!
Sun gleams through
St Michael's heaven
making a rainbow
over Porthleven,
'knew he'd keep his promise,'
says doubting Thomas,
'only a shower,'
says Margaret Dower;
sun like a sprinter
has cleared the winter,
winter twice as dark
and twice as deep
as Pengellow Water*
and harder to leap;
brollies being shaken
in a flurry,
altogether in
the Helston Furry!

*Pengellow Water: formerly men were made to jump this muddy pool, or pay a fine, if they were caught working on the Flora

5

St Michael was soaked to the skin but bubbly with enthusiasm. 'Wasn't it *handsome?*' he enthused. The Devil pulled a long face. 'The organisers are ruining it,' he said; adding brightly,'thank goodness. Tacking things on that didn't use to be there. There was no Children's Dance in the old days.' 'But that's good,' St Michael protested. 'Folk-customs, like everything else, shouldn't stand still. It's a lovely idea to let the children join in.' Then he recalled a bone he had to pick with the Devil. 'Why did you push that lady? That was stupid – she was very nice.'

'*Nice!*' sneered the Devil. 'There's not anything anywhere that's nice. The whole planet's going to the dogs, I'm delighted to say.'

They got into an argument about who was winning, Good or Evil, God or the Devil. 'We've got an hour or so before the next Dance,' said the Devil, 'let's fly around a bit and I'll prove I'm winning.'

'Well, I can do with slipping out of this wet body,' agreed the Angel. 'But I'll prove *He's* winning ...'

They rose swiftly and flew inland. In the grey day old disused tin-mines thrust up their chimney stacks like ghostly warning fingers. Among the yellow gorse and scattered granite boulders they had occasional glimpses of tall standing-stones. The Devil pointed at one. 'Prehistoric sacrifices. Remember? A point to me.'

St Michael nodded towards another. 'Celtic cross. Worshipping God. One to Him.'

The Devil pointed to a more modern cross, in a little village square. 'War memorial,' he said cheerfully. 'Millions killed. Ten points to me at least.' He added slyly, 'Talking of human sacrifices ... I can't think why you like the Flora so much. Really it's *my* dance. Remember when they used to kill a young girl as a sacrifice to me to make sure their crops grew?'

'That was thousands of years ago, they soon gave it up.'

'When your lot did a take-over, and turned them into a load of softies!' A dreamy look came in the Devil's eyes as he recalled the olden days, the Celtic Beltane festival on May 1st, immediately following Walpurgis Night when all the witches flew on broomsticks ... He saw the crimson Beltane flames leaping, and heard the cries of agony ... That was good, but then they changed the Flora to May 8th, the Feast of the Apparition of St Michael, and the whole thing had gone soft as mushy peas.

They swooped over a field where there were many stones in a circle. Cows grazed quietly nearby. The stones were called Nine Maidens. 'Remember?' asked the Devil. 'Nine beautiful sisters. What were their names? Morwenna, Kerenza, Lowena, Jennifer... I don't recall the rest.   Remember Lowena?'   'She was a handsome little maid, sure enough,' said St Michael.   'I got 'em all into trouble,' said the Devil. 'And God punished them by turning them into stones. A point to me.'

'No,' said St Michael, 'I turned them into stones, to save them from you. Their souls are in Heaven. One to God.'

People say the Nine Maidens were turned into stone because they danced on a Sunday, but it's not quite like that.

They had been good girls at heart, but headstrong. Their father had gone off and left them, and their poor hard-working mother couldn't cope. They wanted pretty clothes which she couldn't afford. The Devil, seeing his chance, had come along and offered them their hearts' desire if they sold their souls to him. They thought it was worth it, because they knew they wouldn't die for years and years and donkey's years. One Sunday evening, instead of going to church as usual, they followed the Devil to a lonely field, and joined him in a Witches' Sabbath. They smeared their bodies in ointment, which he said would make them able to fly; they chanted the Lord's Prayer backwards, and danced wildly round the Devil. Their poor mother, sitting at home, had a vision of what was happening, and she prayed that her daughters would be saved. St Michael flew down, and found Satan just about to pronounce the magic spell that would marry the maidens to him forever. The only way the Angel could save their souls was by turning them into stones. As she danced, Lowena said, 'My

feet are some cold, Jennifer.' 'So are mine,' replied Jennifer. 'I'm cold all over!'
And there the stones are to this day, in a silent circle.

St Michael and the Devil flew on. 'Look at all the little chapels dotted around,'
observed the Angel. 'Built by the old miners with their own hands.' 'Falling down,
most of 'em!' said the Devil. They veered left, back towards the coast. The Devil
reminded the Angel of the wreckers, who used to pick a shipwreck clean of anything
worth having, and never mind the poor drowning sailors. That was only because their
families were starving, said the Angel - and what about all the lifeboatmen who had
given their lives to save others?

'Look at those pink bungalows down there on the cliffs - and that caravan site!
They're awful, *awful!*' said the Devil gleefully. 'They've ruined the coastline.'

'But they can't spoil the sea,' said the Angel. The waters of Mount's Bay were so clear
they could glimpse, as they skimmed the waves, the stone hedges of fields drowned
long ago. 'And take a look at St Michael's Mount, just take a look at that! They
haven't spoiled *she!*' St Michael's Mount, a tiny island crowned by an ancient
monastery, stood like a jewel in the shining waters. It is where the Archangel had
appeared to the Cornish.

'Well, you *would* say that!' the Devil sneered. 'Seeing as how they named it after you.
Mark my words, they'll be turning *that* into a hotel next!   For rich oil-men when
they start drilling in the sea round here! I'll give you a point just for now, but that
makes me… still nine ahead, and we've hardly started.'

'But remember our fight,' said St Michael quietly. 'That more than evens the score, I
suggest.'

Because St Michael and the Devil *had* fought, many moons ago. It happened like
this…

6

Hearing that Satan was planning to take over Helston, St Michael had flown straight from Heaven. Sure enough, he found the Devil, in the shape of a huge red flying dragon, poised to swoop on the town. The townsfolk, as you can imagine, were frightened to death, cowering under kitchen tables or kneeling in the streets begging for mercy. To their joy, they saw the Angel in his purple cloak, the sun flashing from his splendid gold wings, his spear at ready, flying from the south straight at the Devil. The Devil, gnashing his teeth, flickering his forked tongue, roaring like thunder, turned round in the sky to face his enemy. He belched a jet of fire, but St Michael's lance pierced his breast, which spouted a cascade of green blood. (You can still see the stain, in the lovely serpentine rocks around the Lizard coast.) Roaring with pain now, the Devil-dragon sped north to Hell's Mouth, near Portreath, and seized in his jaws the lid of Hell, a great rock. He shot it at the Angel with all the force of his fiery breath, at the speed of light. But St Michael had lightning-swift reflexes - as we saw when he dived to save Mrs Winterthrush's glasses - and he moved out of the way in the nick of time. The rock struck him a glancing blow on the shoulder, and fell harmlessly into the centre of Helston.

The enraged Dragon dashed down to Hell, and the breathless crowds gazing up at the contest threw their hats in the air and started to dance for joy through the streets. And that is how some people say the Furry dance began, but we know that it started many, many years before that ... And that is also how some people say Helston got its name - Hell-stone ... But other, very dull people say it isn't so, and they are probably right.

St Michael remembered his victory with quiet satisfaction. 'I guess that was worth about ten points to me, wouldn't you say?'

'Not at all,' said the Devil, 'look what they used the rock for - built a pub around it!'

And it's true: you can see the Devil's stone in the west wall of the Angel Hotel, right in the centre of Helston.

St Michael smiled wryly. He had to admire the Devil's quick wit. For a few moments he felt warm towards him, as in the old days.

They flew back across Mount's Bay towards the Lizard Point, in the increasingly bright sky. The Devil grudgingly allowed a point for the still-unspoiled beauty of Kynance Cove, its tall and spiky serpentine cliffs glittering with many colours in the sun; and another for the quiet charm of Porthleven, fishing-boats bobbing cheerfully in the harbour. But spotting the saucer-shape of the Satellite Tracking Station on Goonhilly Downs, he gleefully claimed ten points for himself. 'Look what television and computers are doing to the kids!' he said. 'Half of them were falling asleep while they were dancing, this morning! Goggle-eyed, they are!'

They coasted towards Helston in silence for a while. The Devil stole a sly sidelong glance. 'Mind you,' he said, 'there was one kid in the dance who's got something - a bit extra ... I suppose you noticed?'

'Of course,' said the Angel, casually. 'Cora Tremaine. Aunt Mary Moses, with the Summer in her body. She ought to have led the Hal-an-Tow, but nobody knows who she is.'

There's always one girl who's a bit special, who will do something exceptional –an Aunt Mary Moses – even if the townsfolk don't know it.

'No doubt you've put a charm around her?' the Devil sneered.

'Not having you getting at her.'

'Shame!'

Drifting down, they had a bird's eye view of the packed, excited streets lined with stalls; the top hats and floral dresses assembling in front of the Guildhall; the sun flashing on the band-instruments. The Devil said, why didn't they join in the dance? It would be a bit of fun. 'I can easily find us a couple of partners,' he winked. St Michael was tempted. He fancied a bit of a dance. But no - he knew the Devil's way of 'finding' a couple of partners. They'd be women with a bit of the Devil in them. 'Why don't we join the band?' he suggested. 'They've usually had a few drinks by this time. They won't notice two extras and they can do with some help. Make a nice change for an hour or two, in the warm sunshine.'

'Okay. I fancy the tuba.'

'I'll play a trumpet, ' said the Angel. They jostled into place just as the Town Clock struck twelve and the drummer banged his big drum to start the main Furry Dance.

7

Derek Pemberthy
stocky and swarthy
Amy by his side
town's newest bride,
William John Billing
has got a shilling
the former Mrs Paull
will spend it all,
Meneage St. to Wendron
bright sun overhead,
the first four dancers
Helston-bred,
morning suits, top hats,
flower in the lapel,
all the handsome women
dressed just as well,
just as well dressed
as ladies in France,
altogether in
the Furry Dance!
Jack Penaluna
should've turned sooner
Jack's wife Kit
had to wait a bit,
laughing Sammy Wood
feeling very good
someone else's wife
(his own's in Fife)
give her hand a twirl
and then take Kit's
Kitty's good as gold
But Jack has fits
same old tune
played the same as ever,
cornet getting worse as
he's not too clever,
two notes behind
but what's the hurry?
altogether in
the Helston Furry!
Out of Messrs Bowdens

down the Market steps,
an arm for Mrs Bone
or she might collapse,
hot as Hell's Kitchen,
corset getting tight,
Rita John little on,
she's all right,
glad of the shade, you,
louder and faster,
frighten the budgie,
mind the plaster,
granny looking old,
she won't be long,
nice place for someone
buy it for a song,
mind the dog-droppings,
turn, and advance,
altogether in
the Furry Dance!
Winking Denzil Brown
biggest rogue in town,
Jennifer Eathorne
pure as the hawthorn,
haughty Tommy Beer
not quite here
cousin Lois Moyle
fried in cooking oil,
Lord, how much farther?
-right to the end,
husband by wife
and friend by friend,
turn and turn about
and hand in hand,
where to, next, you?
follow the band,
in at the wrong door,
sorry sir and madam,
don't expect in Cornwall
Eve and Adam,
boom boom boom boom
never a glance,
altogether in
the Furry Dance!

Mr Malgrue
had a glass or two
Mrs Tremaine
will never complain
but Mrs Rudge-Brown
who's wearing a frown,
is glad Mr Rudge
is sober as a judge,
Lady St., Bowling Green,
crowds spinning by,
nice bit of stuff, that,
caught his eye,
faces like pumpkins
the colour of sherry,
altogether in
the Helston Furry!
Tonight Mr Hocking
won't need rocking
Mrs Hocking though
skips like a doe,
James Henry Blight
high as a kite
his old wife Kitty
never felt so pretty,
open the doors
on all the blind,
unlock the heart and
blow the mind,
chase the ghosts
from winter s corners
the Helston dead
don't want mourners,
want to clap a dance
by the survivors,
trumpet through Barclays
blow away the fivers,
ache tomorrow, but
we don't worry,
altogether in
the Helston Furry!
Getting even hotter
in the hurling sun,
hemmed by crowds and

crushed to one another,
giggling, laughing
puffing, panting,
  slipping, tripping,
    sweat streaming
      flesh steaming,
        high heels stumbling,
          hair-do's tumbling,
            one and all together
              yet two by two,
                all the town rocking
                  so why don't you?
                    whirl your girl around
                    for richer for poorer,
                  altogether in
                the Helston Flora!

8

'That was great!' said the Angel, snapping his fingers and making his trumpet vanish. 'Gabriel would have loved it –he can make the trumpet talk, old Gaby can. Fancy a drink?'

They pushed their way into a crowded pub. He ordered a glass of lemonade to cool himself down, and the Devil, a brandy to warm himself up. Even wearing a thick uniform and blowing a tuba for miles under the warm May sun, he had felt chilly. He felt even chillier now, because the sun had gone in.

'Typical!' he said. 'Sleet for the Servants' Dance at seven o'clock this morning, and I bet it'll bucket down for the Workers' Dance at five, but lovely weather for the Posh People's Dance in between! It's terrible class-distinction anyway, the whole show. I ought to get a few points for that.'

'Rubbish!' said the Angel, smiling at a flushed and harassed bar maid. 'It might have been true once, but not any more. People haven't got any servants, and they're better off than when I was last here. Remember the children dressed in rags, no shoes to their feet, put out to work at ten or eleven? That's gone, I'm glad to say.' He thought of claiming a few points, but he was tired of the stupid contest.

'That may be so,' said the Devil, 'as far as Helston is concerned. I was in Africa last week, and you should see the children there…'. St Michael nodded, troubled. 'And in any case,' the Devil argued, 'are these kids any happier? Take Cora Tremaine. Dad disappeared, stepdad a drunken layabout, mum working every night in a pub. Not much life for a kid.' The Devil could see from St Michael's face that he had struck another shrewd blow. He kept up the attack.

'What a crew we had dancing behind us! Drunks, skinflints, shop-lifters, child-batterers!' St Michael opened his mouth to protest, but the Devil was in full flood. 'And look at the houses we went through! How many animals died in agony to give Colonel Huntley-Staggs all those stuffed heads! And did you see old Granny Craze, smiling in her rocking-chair? Dear old soul, she is! Wouldn't hurt a fly! Good as gold! They don't know she sticks pins in wax dolls to give people illnesses, do they? The whole thing's a sham. You're just soft!' His eyes glittered as he gulped his tea.

St Michael, knowing he was on the defensive, tried to turn the tables by asking the Devil if he hadn't enjoyed the Dance -all the jolly warm-hearted comradeship? 'No of course you didn't,' he said, answering his own question.

'Not enough action,' said the Devil. 'Too tame. Why in Heaven's name - Hell's name

4

- have they dropped the Hurling? That was fun.' The Devil was referring to a primitive kind of rugby football, played once upon a time all over Cornwall, and to this day in the town of St Columb. In Helston, the hurling had taken place on May 2nd. The ball was a wooden globe cased in silver, and the 'goals' were miles apart. There weren't many rules ... The object was simply, by fair means or foul, to carry the ball to the goal. At the start, the silver globe was thrown high in the sky, then when it fell to ground with a thump someone would grab it and run off through the streets. When he was tackled, by two or three or a dozen opponents crunching him to the ground, he would try to fling the ball forward, but perhaps one of the enemy would seize it this time, and set off careering towards the opposite goal. To and fro the battle raged for hours, till some fleet-footed farmer, fisherman or miner would outstrip everyone and hare to the goal. The ball would belong to him for the next year.

At the end of the contest, the streets groaned like a battlefield. If there weren't actually limbs lying about, there were broken bones in plenty. And there weren't any substitutes, because all the townsmen took part. Yet in many ways it was a very chivalrous game. Even in the heat of battle, with steam rising from the wrestling bodies as if it was a cattle-market, some old lady might lean out of an upstairs window and ask to touch the ball. And they would stop and toss it up to her, for her to hold it reverently for a few moments, perhaps for the last time in her life . . . Because the silver ball was magic, and life-giving, like the sun is. And sometimes, a young man would toss the ball up for his wife or sweetheart to fondle, which would bring them good luck.

But the Devil didn't care about such pleasant customs, he was only interested in the violence. 'Four broken skulls, the last time I was here!' he said, with a grin.

'Why don't you go and jump in Loe Pool?' said the Angel. 'Visit your old girlfriend!' This was a deep, murky lake, near Helston, where an enchantress, Morgan le Fay, lives. The Devil barked a laugh. 'Done that yesterday,' he said. 'Old crow! Took her to the Flora Cinema to see a disaster movie. Great it was!'

St Michael excused himself and left. Time was precious. Even living for ever, there was too much to do and see. He slipped out of his band uniform, and rose like an eagle, flying east this time. He followed the winding and dreaming Helford River, to the sea, then turned into Falmouth harbour where there were ships flying the flags of all nations. Unfortunately the cloud which had drizzled on the Children's Dance had reached Falmouth and was hovering over the town. Here it wasn't Flora Day, just a damp grey miserable Tuesday. In Marks & Spencer, bored housewives were shopping. They looked grumpy and cheesed-off. Everything was too dear! And the salesgirls were grumpy too, grabbing the held-out purchases and stuffing them in paper-bags.

But suddenly everyone stood stock still, and their mouths fell open. They heard, over the loudspeaker, the merry brassy notes of the Floral Dance . . . And immediately, all over the store, garments started to come alive, trousers slipped off hangers, shirts crashed out of cellophane packets and scattered pins on the counters ... And all the different male and female garments joined themselves up, in the right places, formed a double line down one aisle, and jigged and jogged to the catchy tune, in and out and round about the various counters, brushing past the dumbfounded shoppers and salesgirls.

... jackets and ties
and coloured shirts,
polyester dresses
or blouses and skirts,
pyjamas and nighties,
tights and pants,
altogether in
St Michael's Dance! ...

The CD recording stopped. The clothes vanished back into their packets and onto their hangers. But before anyone could say 'Well I never!' they saw, towering above the food counters, the proud and awesome figure of an Angel in a purple cloak, his wings furled. He calmed their fright with a smile. 'Cheer up!' he cried. 'It may never happen! Cornwall for ever! Oggy! Oggy! Oggy!' Then he vanished. The shoppers and salesgirls started moving as before, buying and selling, and strange to relate they did not remember anything of what had happened. The only difference was that, now, they all felt curiously elated. 'It's goin' to brighten up!' they were saying, glancing out. They carried this cheerfulness out into the street to all the other shoppers in Falmouth. Everybody on the right hand side of the street kept shouting out 'Oggy! Oggy! Oggy!' and everybody on the left hand side shouted back joyfully, 'Oy! Oy! Oy!' They didn't know why they did it, but it was very enjoyable.

As St Michael coasted back to Helston he saw a helicopter hovering over the Guildhall, and a young man swinging out on to a rope-ladder. It was Lance-Corporal Blamey, home with his battalion from Iraq. His flight had been held up, and a helicopter-pilot from HMS Seahawk had very kindly given him a lift to make sure he made the five o'clock dance on time. 'Blimey, there's Blamey!' exclaimed his friend Percy Trengrouse, as the red beret swung agilely down the swaying rope-ladder. Isobel Bone clapped her hands in relief. She wasn't going to be a wallflower after all!

9

Percy Trengrouse is
a painter of houses
saves some paint for Rose
who paints her toes,
Paratrooper Blamey
on leave from the army
fallen like a stone
for Isobel Bone,
the five o'clock Furry
gets under way,
the sun going down
but here to stay,
everyone who wants to
can join the line,
even Mrs Winterthrush
looking fine,
dancing with a youngster
in tee-shirt and jeans
who's dancing with a nurse
from Indian Queens
who twists Mr Winterthrush
round and round,
the trumpets blare
and the drum-beats pound,
he's lost his money
but he doesn't worry,
altogether in
the Helston Furry!
'Honey, this is fun,
I'm having a ball!'
(a kiss-me-quick hat
he's bought at a stall)
'I'm giving up funerals,
there ain't no death,
they're nothing but dancers
out of breath,
we'll buy a little store
selling angel cakes
knickerbocker glories
and pink milk shakes,'

28

open your doors
let the Angel through,
hallway and dining-room
kitchen and loo,
summer's fetched home,
hot as a curry –

I've had about enough of the blasted Furry, thought the Devil. I'm off. Take a walk. Get my circulation going. He could have joined in the dancing with the Angel but he didn't see there was anything at all to celebrate. What an idiot St Michael looked, laughing with that young nurse and Mrs Winterthrush, and sucking a stick of rock! The streets were still packed with onlookers, who rushed from one street to the next to get another view. He couldn't imagine how anybody could be so stupid.

The sun had gone in again. In spite of his layers of thermal underwear, band uniform, duffel coat and Wellingtons, he was freezing, since he was used to a really hot climate. He set off for the fairground at the bottom end of the town. A fair was always good for a laugh.

It was a relief to have a change of music anyway. He enjoyed the noise made by all the different pop-tunes coming from different rides, and the screaming sirens when the rides ended. Everyone seemed to be having a good time, but he could soon throw a spanner in the works. Even with St Michael in town, there was enough power in him to get a laugh. He made the youth manning the Waltzers pull his lever a bit too hard, and send the machine into an even faster whirl. Everyone shrieked, excited and afraid, and clung on to the bar for grim death. When the young man with the lever corrected his mistake, a few of the passengers were white-faced and looked sick. The Devil went to the Dodgems and worked the electric so that the cars speeded up and couldn't help colliding with each other head-on, which gave the riders some nasty jolts. He sent a noise like a thousand thunder-claps through young Kim Treloar's mobile phone, just as she was calling her Mum, and she jumped three feet in the air. He made the Big Wheel move in jerks, shaking the cars and scaring the customers. He went into the Hall of Mirrors and made Denzil Brown see horns and fangs when he looked at his reflection -Denzil reeled back in surprise, and his girlfriend Jennifer Eathorne changed from a laugh to a scream as she also had a look.

Old Mr and Mrs Blight gave their grandson Jimmy a pound to go on the Ghost Train with his friend Tony, while they themselves thought they'd try the Tunnel of Love. It was something they hadn't done since they had led the midday Flora, fifty years ago, and they were as excited as kids. It seemed like a second honeymoon! Kitty Blight settled her rheumatic old bones in the boat, and James Henry plumped wheezing down beside her. He paddled off into the darkness.

'This is handsome, you!' he said, taking Kitty's hand. 'Brought the Malteasers, have 'ee?' 'Ess. Here you are, my lover. This do take me back some years, James Henry,' sighed Kitty. 'Put your arm around me.' 'Tisn't too warm, is it?' said her husband. 'In fact it's bloomin' chilly. Must be the damp walls. Don't catch your death of cold. Good job you got your woolly vest on.' 'Never mind that,' said Kitty, 'I do never feel cold when you're beside me. You're as warm as toast, my lover.' (The Cornish like calling people 'my lover,' and 'my sweetheart', 'my bird', 'my cock', and 'my handsome', and it doesn't mean necessarily that they love them; in fact they may never have seen them before in their lives. Though in this case Mr and Mrs Blight did love each other.)

Just then, as they drifted in the dark tunnel, a grinning white skeleton danced in front of them, and Mrs Blight threw her arms around James Henry. A blood-curdling scream rang out and echoed along the tunnel. A huge spider's web brushed past their faces. Ghostly lights flashed on and off; from beneath the boat came an evil chuckle. Devil masks loomed up and floated by.

When they came out into the open air, Mr Blight climbed slowly out, and then helped his wife up. They both looked pale and shaky. Mr Blight spoke to the ticket-salesman: 'Very romantic, I must say.'

Denzil Brown and Jennifer Eathorne were about to climb in a boat. 'Tunnel of Love worth it is it, Mr Blight?' he asked - with a wink at Mrs Blight. 'Worth every penny,' said Mr Blight. 'Go on in and enjoy yourselves. You won't want to come out!'

Their grandson and his pal emerged from the Ghost Train, looking delighted with themselves. 'Didn't scare me a bit, Gran,' Jimmy said, puffing out his chest proudly. 'Pitch black 'twas, excep' for coloured lights, and there were these - like, naked midgets on the walls firin' arrows. Didn't scare me, though.' Jimmy and Tony ran off to find Jenny and Cora and have a row on the Boating Lake, which adjoined the fair-field.

The Devil watched the children paddling on the Lake. His eyes were fixed on the boat which held Cora Tremaine and her friends. The light was fading on the murky water and he felt more at home. The clouds overhead were dark-grey and had more rain in them, and a strong breeze had blown up. He wondered why the kids weren't freezing to death, in their light white summer dresses and white shirts and shorts. He envied their carefree happiness, and a pang shot through his heart. He gazed at Cora. There was nothing special about her to look at. Just a normal lively girl, with brown pigtails. He noticed when she laughed her front teeth were askew. He had to admit she had quite attractive, wide hazel eyes, and a sort of a pleasant mouth, but otherwise she wasn't particularly pretty. Jenny Rame, on the other hand, would be a real stunner in a few years. It was funny, thought the Devil, you could never tell, from one generation to the next, who would be Aunt Mary Moses - who, for Helston, would carry in her body and heart and mind the power of the sun, the warmth of the Summer. Usually they didn't even know it themselves. Cora certainly didn't.

Years and years and donkey's years ago, before Christian times, she would have known, sure enough! His eyes grew dreamy again as he remembered the Beltane Fire leaping on Hangman's Barrow, and the frightened maiden, decked in flowers, riding a donkey, leading the procession up the slope, as the townsfolk fetched the Summer home... He recalled many a May Queen, fainting with terror, being helped down from the donkey and dragged along the ground to the fire. Old women had been burnt too, and men, not to mention hundreds of cats and chickens, frying nicely ... but it was the May Queens he liked to recall, their lovely faces twisted in agony as the flames crackled and leapt, and the circle of savages prayed aloud for good crops this year...

Dearly he would have loved to overtopple the boat, give Cora at least a good dunking. But with St Michael's charm around her, she and her friends were safe. He ground his teeth in frustration. He tried to exert his power, but failed completely The children went on paddling happily, ignoring the man who stood on the bank watching them.

The Devil had had enough of Helston. But he fancied one slap-up meal before flying off to another town. He walked rather tiredly back uphill towards the town centre - why were Cornish towns always so hilly? It quite put a Devil off coming on holiday.

Passing a terrace of drab grey houses, he heard the thump of a jolly piano and a booming bass voice. Peeping cautiously through the window he saw an enormously fat lady in a floral dress overflowing a piano stool, and a short, stocky man in morning suit standing behind her, looking over her shoulder at the sheet of music, and bellowing away for all he was worth. The Devil recognised them from the midday dance; they were Mr and Mrs Bone. Their fat son Tommy was sitting in an armchair eating a huge pasty. Two other dancers, Mr and Mrs Penaluna, were sipping cups of tea and listening to the song. It was difficult not to listen to it, as the furniture was vibrating, Mr Bone was so loud and deep. Even from outside, the Devil could hear it clearly. 'That blasted tune again! ' he growled to himself. 'Can't get away from it...'

Indeed it was the same Furry Dance tune, basically, though with pleasant extra variations thrown in, and words added. Just about everybody in the whole world has heard it, and it goes like this ...

THE FLORAL DANCE

As I walked home on a summer night
When stars in heaven were shining bright
Far away from the footlights' glare
Into that sweet and scented air
Of a quaint old Cornish town,

Borne from afar on a gentle breeze
Joining the murmur of summer seas,
Distant tones of an old world dance,
Played by the village band perchance,
On the calm air came floating down.

Chorus:
I thought I could hear the curious tone
Of the cornet, clarinet, and big trombone,
Fiddle, cello, big bass drum,
Bassoon, flute, and euphonium,
Each one making the most of his chance,
All together in the Floral Dance!
And soon I heard such a bustling and prancing
And then I saw the whole village was dancing.
In and out of the houses they came,
Old folk, young folk, all the same,
In that quaint old Cornish town,
Every boy took a girl round the waist
And hurried her off at tremendous haste,
Whether they knew one another I care not,
Whether they cared at all I know not,
But they kissed as they danced along.

Chorus:
And there was the band with the curious tone ...

I felt so lonely standing there,
And I could only stand and stare,
For I had no maid with me,
Lonely I should have to be
In that quaint old Cornish town,
When suddenly hastening down the lane
A figure I knew I saw quite plain,
With outstretched arms I rushed along,
And carried her into that happy throng,
While fiddle and all came dancing down.

Chorus:
We danced to the band with the curious tone
Of the cornet, clarinet, and big trombone,
Fiddle, cello, big bass drum,

Bassoon, flute, and euphonium,
Each one making the most of his chance,
All together in the Floral Dance!
Dancing here, prancing there,
Jigging, jogging everywhere,
Up and down and around the town,
Hurrah for the Cornish Floral Dance!

The Devil hated it, but was held spellbound by Mr Bone's booming voice, and also by the way Mrs Bone, fat as a pig, could play all the quick twiddly bits with such a feather-soft touch. When they had finished performing, Mrs Penaluna said what a handsome voice he had, 'he should be on the stage'. And so should Mrs Bone, her husband chimed in –picturing Mrs B rolling on to a stage. Looking pleased as punch, Mr Bone said it was a handsome song; and Mrs Bone, taking a gulp of tea, said she'd read in the West Briton that the author, a Miss Katie Moss, had written the song eighty or more years ago, on the train coming back from holiday in Cornwall. 'Some clever woman she must have been, ' said Mr Penaluna.

Then Mrs Penaluna requested Mr Bone to sing the song once more. Mr Bone beamed. The Devil could hardly believe his ears. They wanted that blasted tune again! They must have heard it a hundred and fifty times already today. He knew Mr Penaluna suffered from fits, and he'd be likely to have one, with that great voice booming out. That might be an interesting sight... He thought he'd play another little jape. When Mr Bone reached the first chorus, the words that actually spilled from his gaping mouth were - not the right words at all - but these:

'I danced and I held on to Mrs Bone,
And I wished I danced in the streets alone,
Twice as heavy as a big bass drum,
I'd swop her for a euphonium.. . '

Mr Bone's mouth gaped even wider and Mrs Bone almost fell back off her piano stool. The Devil chuckled as he watched them wrangling, with Mr. Bone explaining that he just didn't know why those words had come out of his mouth, it must have been a brainstorm. Tommy Bone, covered in pasty flakes, was roaring with laughter, doubled up. Mr and Mrs Penaluna were trying to soothe their host and hostess. Fortunately there was a good excuse to let the argument simmer down, as Kitty Penaluna reminded them that it was nearly time for the Flora Day programme on the telly. There was going to be a big news report on the day's events in Helston, and all day they'd been excited at the thought of seeing themselves. Mr Bone gratefully clicked on the remote, and everyone sat around in front of the screen. The Devil was quite curious too, and lingered outside the window to watch. It came on almost at once. After a few shots of the Hal-an-Tow singers fetching the Summer home, they saw the children assembling outside the school. 'There you are, Tommy!' said his mother excitedly, and Tommy leaned forward till he was almost inside the set. By a bit of bad luck the camera brought him into close-up just as he was picking his nose. When his mother scolded him, Tommy protested that he was sure he hadn't picked his nose.

The Devil suddenly had a brilliant idea. It wasn't possible to do any mischief to Cora Tremaine direct, face to face, because of the charm that was around her. But just as the old witches like Granny Craze hurt people by making images of them out of wax, and then sticking pins in them, it might be possible to hurt the child by a roundabout way. And what better way than through the telly? Not a wax image but a television image! He could see her mingling with the other children, and being told off by her teacher for looking dozy. It would be splendid to do some harm to her, and so, for once in his life, turn the Summer back into winter... He made himself invisible, and flew quick as light up over Helston and away over Goonhilly. He hovered over the Satellite Tracking Station. There, over that great powerful saucer searching the sky, he could make anything happen, on any TV screen in the world ...

And meanwhile, back at the Angel Hotel, St Michael had been having a whale of a time. The bar was heaving with happy people, hot and thirsty after the dance, and the Angel was buying them all a round of drinks. 'Bitter lemon, my sweetheart!' he said to the shy nurse from Indian Queens, passing her the glass. 'Bloody Mary coming over, my lover!' he called to Maude Winterthrush, who replied, 'You're an angel, honey!' 'Scotch on the rocks, my handsome!' he said to Horace Winterthrush. The American couple were smiling all over their faces. St Michael was delighted he had exerted his power and persuaded the Devil to lift Mr Winterthrush's wallet. Without his money to weigh him down, he was a really nice person.

'And take one for yourself, my sweetheart,' he said to the barmaid - Cora's mother. She said she was sweating quarts, and would join him in a cool shandy, thanking him with a friendly smile. The Angel was glad she was jolly and warm-hearted. At least

Cora wouldn't lack for love: even though her good-for-nothing stepfather, Mr Malgrue, was slumped at the other end of the bar, well out of it. St Michael also liked the barmaid's low-cut evening blouse, and he looked at her figure appreciatively. That was one thing he envied men - women! Women were so warm and pleasant.

The room was buzzing with jokes and laughter and good fellowship. The Angel was wearing Lance-Corporal Blamey's red beret, and he had his arm around Isobel Bone, teasing her about her 'spare tyre'. 'You watch what you're doin' with my girlfriend, Mike!' Lance Corporal Blamey called good-humouredly. Mrs Tremaine, glancing at the wall-clock, picked up the remote to switch on the huge TV set in the corner. The bar grew hushed. All eyes turned to the screen, eager to pick out their own son or daughter, or perhaps a grandchild, as the Children's Dance began for the second time that day…

11

Kim Treloar
the same as before
Linda Tregonning
the same as this morning
give us a vision of
dancing feet,
then the happy faces, all
the dancing street,
glimpse of St Michael's
Church up above,
people still go there
f or death or love;
turn back, time,
see you even better,
this morning the air
seemed duller and wetter;
'Tim looks nice, dear'
(the little horror)
altogether in
the BBC Flora!
'Hasn't she grown, June!'
'Well I never!'
same old tune and
played the same as ever,
bring up the soundtrack,
boom boom BOOM,
cut to the kids again,
pan and zoom,
highlight the tresses
where the highlights are
cut to a black cat
– blessed telly-star! –
running from the Chinese
takeaway, Wun Lung,
(never says a word,
cat got his tongue)
June's daughter Cora
trips on the cat,
almost sends her flying –
Don't remember that!

Instantly and in a flash St Michael was out of the hotel. They were so engrossed they didn't notice he had disappeared ...

At the same instant, Cora Tremaine was walking up the road from the Fair, giggling with her friends, telling jokes. They strolled four abreast, and she was on the outside, doing the Furry skip along the cat's-eyes ... She wished every day could be Flora Day.

At the same instant, young Denzil Brown, having dropped his girlfriend home to change, had picked up a beautiful red-head from the Angel Hotel and was zooming down Coinagehall Street in his nippy red sports car. She was a friend of one of the television camera crew. What a bit of luck he'd spotted her in the crowds! They could have a nice spin out to Porthleven, stroll around the harbour, and he'd still be back in time to take Jennifer to the Ball. He showed off by revving straightway to seventy - all the coppers and traffic-wardens would be watching the box – and roared down-hill, tyres screaming as he took the tight bends. There was a sputter of rain on the windscreen. 'Raining again!' he groaned. 'Blimey, it's hailing!' Hailstones cascaded against the windscreen, blanketing it: he saw the figure too late, and turned cold as the weather turned ...

Cora stood turned to stone in the hailstorm, blinded by headlights, deafened by the roar . . . A young man in a red beret, her guardian angel, scooped her up in his arms like lightning, almost under the screaming wheels, and placed her gently on the pavement. Denzil climbed from his car, his face whiter than the white road. 'Are you all right, my handsome?' he asked her. The child nodded. He hugged her, and breathed a prayer of thanksgiving. The hail-shower had stopped. The evening sun struggled to break through the cloud.

12

St Michael rose from the town, moving his strong gold wings, his purple cloak
streaming out behind him in the sea-breeze. He burned for vengeance. All his
gentleness had gone; now he was once again God's warrior. Anger sped him faster
than light, and he soon glimpsed the Devil, a fiery winged dragon, flying towards the
horizon. Whenever his most evil plans were thwarted, he turned into a dragon.
Seeing the Angel in pursuit, he turned and tried to send a warning belch of flame;
but the effort of manifesting the witch's cat on television had drained his power, and
all that came out of his mouth was a spark, like a lighter that's run out of fuel.

The cloud had cleared, leaving a fresh, pale-blue, rapidly fading sky. The sun was dropping towards thin fleecy clouds on the horizon. The Devil was racing across Mount's Bay, and St Michael could see his shadow on the shining sea. When he 'lost' the Devil temporarily against the round red sun, St Michael kept following the shadow. Then the Dragon wheeled to the right, and struck again inland, northwards - heading for Hell's Mouth, a beetling sinister cliff where the ghosts of drowned sailors cry in the gulls.

He loomed large now; St Michael could see the scales on the winding, churning tail, could see the flickering, venomous tongue. The dragon was struggling to keep up his speed, flagging badly, sinking through the air - looked as if he would crash into the slopes of Carn Brea. St Michael was almost upon him. Then – just as he was drawing his sword ready to plunge it into his enemy - the Devil was gone again: he had slipped into the disused shaft of Dolcoath tin-mine. St Michael followed, plunging into the murky depths of the shaft. Darker and darker it grew, deeper and deeper. St Michael could not see the Devil but he could hear his hoarse gasps. At the bottom of the shaft the Devil sheered off into one of the mine-levels. It was flooded with rusty water, and this impeded the Angel's progress. It grew so narrow, after a while, it was like squeezing through a tube. Mile after mile they went, hunter and hunted.

The ground was like a honeycomb, eaten away by the work of thousands of miners, a hundred and more years ago. The Devil tried to trick St Michael by twisting and turning through the maze of tunnels, but always he heard the Angel at his back. He began to despair.

St Michael followed him up through another shaft, out on the other side of the granite, honeycombed hill. When he rose out of the darkness like a rocket, he saw to his surprise and annoyance that the Devil had gained on him, and he was also now back in his more usual shape, a horned and cloven-footed angel. The black heat of the deep mine had re-charged him, given him fresh energy, whereas it had sapped a little of St Michael's strength. Now the contest was more equal. The Devil flew westwards now, down the spine of Cornwall, sparkling sea on either side. The Angel had to use all his strength to keep from falling further behind. But gradually the fresh air revived him, and he saw he was gaining on the Devil again.

The Devil sank down on to the last patch of earth in Britain – Land's End. He was utterly spent. St Michael plummeted to ground near him, and drew his sword. He stood over the Devil, and raised his sword high in the air with both hands. He was aiming for the heart.

His breath rasping like a bellows, the Devil rolled his eyes up towards St Michael. 'Call it a draw?' he said.

St Michael held his sword aloft for a long time, but then let it slowly drop, till its point stood on the rock. A voice told him he shouldn't kill the Devil. It was too easy to destroy. It was much better to try and redeem evil. He had not yet quite given up hope that one day the Devil might repent. Inside all the blackness, there were excellent qualities, including a sense of humour.

The Angel squatted down, and gazed out to sea. All the west was a blaze of crimson. The sun hung near the water's edge, behind faint scarlet strips of cloud. 'Red sky at night, shepherd's delight,' he said. The Devil struggled up into a crouching position too. 'Yes, it's going to be a fine day tomorrow, unfortunately – still, we can't win them all.'

'Shove off,' said St Michael, and the Devil said, 'Gladly!' He flew across the water a short way to a tiny rock, and perched there, facing the shore. He shouted back: 'They tell me you've got to book a year ahead for the Main Flora Dance! It's of no interest to me, but I thought you might like to know ... Bookin' a year in advance, I ask you!'

 St Michael said nothing. He was picturing Aunt Mary Moses in a year's time. She'd have grown even more. He hoped they'd do something to straighten her teeth.

The Devil sang, in a wild and weird voice: 'I danced to the band with the curious tone, Of the cornet, clarinet and big trombone . . . ' He barked a laugh, scattering the seagulls, sending a big breaker in.

'Well,' he said, 'I'll be off, then, Mikey!'

'Cheerio,' said St Michael, after a short silence.

'See you at Michaelmas, perhaps?' said the Devil, and he flew away.

> As the sun dipped his head to sleep
> An Angel on St Michael's Keep
> Looked up to where the summer stars
> Called him to fight in other wars.

Across the bay the Lizard Light
Would keep the peace throughout the night,
A charm for luck. – then disappear.
Nothing to keep the Angel here.

'Demon and Serpent, have no power
To hurt a child, or blight a flower. '
Spoke the charm, and then was gone.
Another star in heaven shone.

And that was fading, as the sky
The fishermen were sailing by
Under the shadow of Kynance
Wheeled in one majestic dance.

THE HELSTON FURRY DANCE, or FLORA

This is the Floral Dance tune played by the Helston Band. It is repeated over and over again as the dancing continues, and grows more and more excited.

(transposed a tone higher)

THE HAL-AN-TOW

This is the tune of the Morning Song, sung by the young people in the Hal-an-Tow as they fetch the Summer home.

Robin Hood and Lit-tle John They both are gone to Fair, _ O, And we will go to the

mer-ry green wood To see what they do there,_ O, And for to _ chase, O, to

Chorus

chase the buck and doe. Hal-an - Tow! Jol-ly Rumble O! For we are up _ as

soon as an - y day,_ O, And for to fetch the sum-mer home, The sum-mer and the

May, _ O, For sum-mer is _ a come, O, And win - ter is a gone, O.

Biographical Notes

D.M.Thomas was born in Redruth, Cornwall, in 1935. After attending Grammar Schools in Redruth and Melbourne, Australia, he was awarded a First in English at New College, Oxford. For many years he was a teacher and lecturer, while writing and publishing poetry. In 1979 he became a full-time writer. He has published seven collections of verse, including The Puberty Tree (1992); thirteen novels, including the modern classic The White Hotel (1981), translated into twenty seven languages; translations of Russian poetry, a biography and a memoir. He has won a Cholmondeley Prize for poetry, the Los Angeles Times fiction prize, and the Orwell Prize for his biography of Solzhenitsyn. His most recent verse collection, Dear Shadows, was published by fal in 2004 and was winner of the Holyer an Gof Award for Outstanding Literary Merit. He lives in Truro. For further information and a bibliography please consult www.dmthomasonline.com

Linda Selby is an illustrator and designer who has lived and worked in Cornwall for 40 years. A career change in the late 90s included an extended period of study at Falmouth College of Art which enabled her to pursue her passion for Art and Design. She now teaches in Cornwall in this field, in addition to freelance illustration work for a London Agent and sources design work locally.